Lindhead School

For Tom
B.G.

First published 1992 by
Walker Books Ltd, 87 Vauxhall Walk, London SE11 5HJ

Text © 1992 Brough Girling
Illustrations © 1992 Arthur Robins

First printed 1992
Printed in Hong Kong by South China Printing Co. (1988) Ltd

British Library Cataloguing in Publication Data
A catalogue record for this book is available from the British Library.

ISBN 0 7445 2167 X

I KNOW AN OLD LADY...
a funny sort of joke book

Written by

BROUGH GIRLING

Illustrated by

ARTHUR ROBINS

WALKER BOOKS
LONDON

I know an old lady who swallowed a fly.

I know an old lady who swallowed a bird.

How absurd to swallow a bird!

I know an old lady who swallowed a cat.

Fancy that, she swallowed a cat!

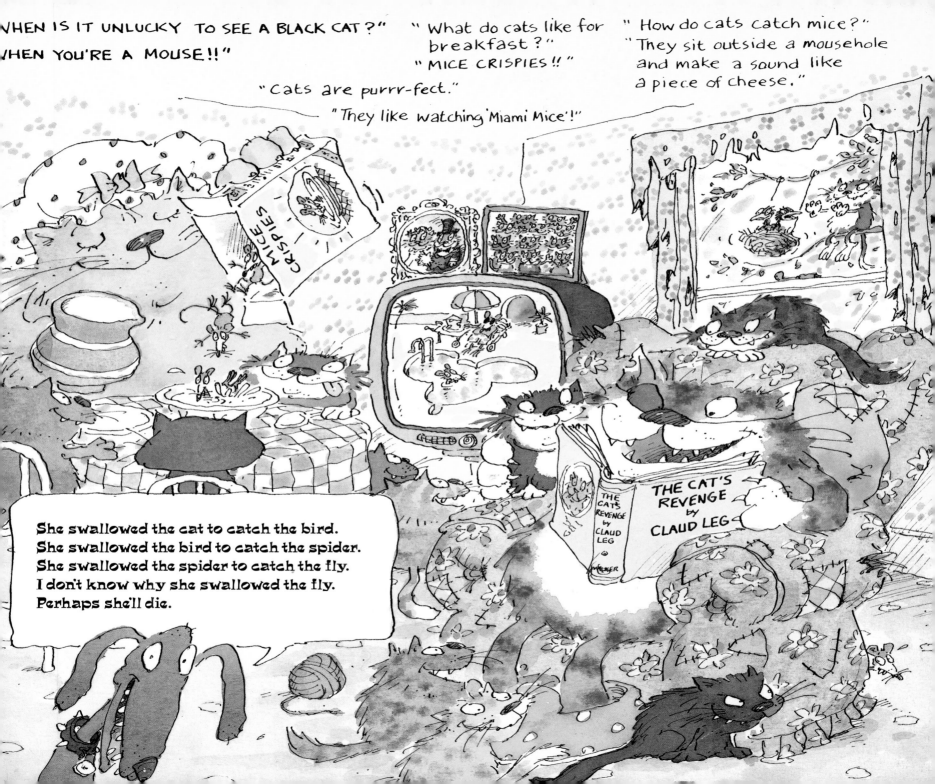

I know an old lady who swallowed a dog.

What a hog, to swallow a dog!

I know an old lady who swallowed a goat.

She just opened her throat and swallowed a goat.

I know an old lady who swallowed a cow.

I don't know how, she just swallowed a cow.

I know an old lady who swallowed a horse.

Then...

Just for a laugh
she ate a giraffe.

Before he could eat her
she swallowed a cheetah.

With no word of excuse
she ate a whole moose.

To continue her meal
she swallowed a seal.

Before he could harm her
she gulped down a llama.

Without knife, fork or spoon
she ate a baboon.

And for pudding she dined on a juicy young lion.

Then it somehow seemed relevant...

to swallow an elephant.

By the time she was through she had swallowed a zoo.

She's dead, of course.